W0041952

"We are going on a magic adventure,"
said Chip.
The children went through the door of the
magic house.
"Oh help!" said Nadim.

The magic took the children to the land of the dinosaurs.

"I don't want this adventure," said Nadim. "I don't want to meet a dinosaur."

A dragonfly flew by.

"Look at this," said Chip. "It's a giant dragonfly. What a big one!"

Chip found a footprint. It was a giant footprint.

"Come and look," said Chip. "It must be a dinosaur's footprint."

Biff took a photograph of the giant footprint.

"I can take this photograph to school," she said.

Nadim found some eggs. They were big eggs.

"They must be a dinosaur's eggs," he said.

One of the eggs began to crack.
"It's going to hatch out," said Biff.
Something came out of the egg.
"It's a little dinosaur," said Nadim.

Something flew by. The children were
frightened.

"What is it?" asked Chip.

"I don't know," said Biff.

The children ran.

"It's a flying dinosaur," said Nadim,

"and it's a big one. Come on, let's hide."

The flying dinosaur flew down to the eggs. It picked up the little dinosaur in its teeth.

"Oh no!" said Biff. "It's going to eat it."
She picked up a stick and ran out.
"Go away!" she yelled.

The dinosaur flew away but Chip was cross with Biff.

"You were silly," he said. "It could have got you."

Wilf ran on and climbed a hill. He
wanted to look for an apatosaurus.
"Come up here Biff," he called. "You
can take a photograph."

Wilf had not climbed on a hill. He
had climbed on a dinosaur and it was
enormous. It looked round at Wilf.

Wilf was frightened.

"Oh help!" he said.

He jumped down and ran.

"Let's get out of here," he called.

"Don't be frightened," said Chip. "It's an apatosaurus. It's like the one in the museum. It won't hurt us."

Biff took a photograph of it.

"What a long neck it's got and what a
long tail!" she said. "I need a bigger
camera."

The apatosaurus ran into the water.

"What an enormous splash!" said Wilf.

Nadim looked frightened.

"Oh help!" he called.

Another dinosaur was coming and it looked very fierce.

"Let's get out of here," yelled Chip.

Biff took a photograph.

"Come on," yelled Chip, "don't stop for that. This one could eat us!"

They began to run away. Wilf's other
shoe came off in the mud. Suddenly, the
key began to glow.

"Just in time!" said Chip.

The magic took the children to Biff's bedroom.

"What an adventure!" said Biff. "I've got some good photographs."

"This is the fierce dinosaur," said Chip. "Did you take its photograph?"

"Yes," said Biff. "Let's tell Mum and Dad."

"I took photographs of dinosaurs," said Biff.

"Oh yes," said Dad. "Well, I'm sorry, I didn't put a film in the camera."